Logic Line-ups

by

Miguel Kagan

illustrated by

Celso Rodriguez

Kagan Publishing

981 Calle Amanecer

San Clemente, CA 92673

(949) 545-6300

1 (800) 933-2667

www.KaganOnline.com

ISBN: 978-1-879097-62-9

Table of Contents

Introduction

Why Play Logic Line-Ups?
• Sharpen Thinking Skills
• Develop Spatial Vocabulary
• Promote Cooperation
• Teambuilding

How to Play
The basic idea is for students to use logic to line up object cards according to clues. On the following pages, you will find detailed instructions for the basic way to play along with some powerful variations based on other Kagan Structures.

When to Play?
There are 12 themes or topics. Outer Space, for example, is one of the 12 themes. If you teach thematically or address one of these topics, integrate these logic activities into your lessons. Or use them any time for fun and to develop thinking skills.

What's In this Book?
• **Problems & Answers:** For each of the 12 themes, the first page has six problems (and answers). Each problem has multiple clues. Use the problem pages to read the clues to your class. Or copy the problem pages for students. If you're handing them out to students, you may want to cover the answers.

Problem Pages

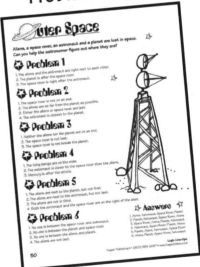

• **Object Cards:** There are both quarter-page cards, and full-page cards. The quarter-page cards are intended for students, teams, or pairs working alone. Copy them onto a sheet of paper and cut the cards apart for sequencing. The full-page cards are for whole class Logic Line-Ups. With the full-page cards, it is easy for you to check at a glance whether or not students are in the correct order.

Make Your Own Problems

There are lots of ready-to-use problems in this book. If you'd like more, you can easily come up with your own problems. Students can also work together to make their own problems and send them to another team to solve. See page 80.

Other Sequencing Ideas

See the list of ideas of other ways to have students sequence their cards. See ideas on page 84.

A Note From the Author

I really enjoyed coming up with these logic problems. I made an effort to make them different in both the type of logic required to find the solution, and the spatial vocabulary. Hopefully they will provide hours of fun and learning for you and your students.

Quarter-Page Object Cards

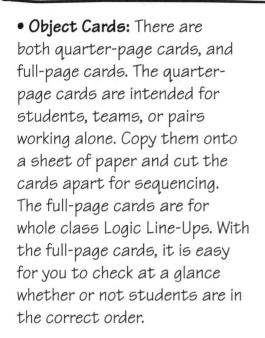

Full-Page Object Cards

Logic Line-Ups

Teammembers each receive a card with a different object. They use deductive thinking to sequence themselves in the correct order according to the clues read by the teacher.

Logic Line-Ups
Kagan Publishing • 1 (800) 933-2667 • www.KaganOnline.com

Set-Up

For each of the 12 themes/topics included in this book, there are four full-page cards. Copy one set of cards for each team of four. The full-page cards are best for teacher-led Logic Line-Ups because it is easy to check team order at a glance.

Steps

1 Teammates Stand
Teammates stand shoulder-to-shoulder, each holding an item card.

2 Teacher Reads First Clue
The teacher reads the first clue to problem one.

3 Check for Agreement
The student mentioned in the clue describes how he/she will line up based on the clue. He/she checks with teammates for agreement. If students disagree, they discuss why.
For example, if the clue was: "The Triceratops is not first or third." The student holding the Triceratops card might say, "I must either be second or last. Do you agree?"

Note: If more than one teammate is mentioned in a clue, they each describe their reasoning and check with teammates for agreement.

4 Teammate(s) Move
The student physically moves to his/her place in the team line up.

5 Teacher Reads Next Clue
After the teacher reads each clue, students repeat Steps 3 and 4.

6 Teacher Selects Team
When all clues have been read and acted on, the teacher calls on one team to describe their order and share their logic.

7 Team Responds
The team selected responds.

8 Teacher Congratulates
The teacher either congratulates the team or provides correction opportunity. Other teams listen and either celebrate or correct their positions.

9 Play Again
The process is repeated for the next problem.

Logic Leader

In this variation of Logic Line-Ups, a teammate is assigned the role of "Logic Leader" for each new problem. The Logic Leader is in charge of directing teammates to line up in the correct order according to the clues read by the teacher.

1 Select Logic Leader
Select a "Logic Leader," one student in each team that will direct his/her team how to line up.

2 Teammates Stand
Teammates stand shoulder-to-shoulder with cards in hand, Logic Leader included.

3 Teacher Reads First Clue
The teacher reads the first clue to problem one.

4 Logic Leader Leads
The Logic Leader states how teammates should line up. He/she asks teammates if they agree.

5 Teammate(s) Move
If teammates agree, they physically move according to the Logic Leader's instructions. If teammates don't agree, they discuss why. The final decision is up to the Logic Leader.

6 Teacher Reads Next Clue
After the teacher reads each clue, students repeat Steps 4 and 5.

7 Teacher Selects Team
When all clues have been read and acted on, the teacher calls on one team.

8 Logic Leader Responds
The Logic Leader shares the sequence and his/her reasoning.

9 Teacher Congratulates
The teacher either congratulates the team or provides correction opportunity. Other teams listen and either celebrate or correct their positions.

10 Play Again
A new Logic Leader is selected for the next problem and the process is repeated.

Other Structures

Numbered Heads Together

The teacher writes the problem on the board, uses a projector, or gives each team a set of problems. Students work in teams to solve the problem assigned. Their goal is to make sure everyone knows the correct answer, and more importantly, how to solve the problem. When teams signal they are ready, the teacher randomly selects one student on one team to give the answer and the reasoning behind the answer.

RallyCoach

Students are in pairs. Student A reads the first clue and describes how to line up the cards accordingly. If Student B agrees, Student A moves the cards. If they disagree, they discuss why. They switch roles for the next clue. Student B describes his/her thinking, then moves the cards when they reach consensus. Partners continue taking turns reading and acting on each clue.

Showdown

Students sit in small teams. Without talking, students solve the first logic problem. When teammates signal they are done, one student calls, "Showdown." Teammates each show their answers and check that they all agree. If they disagree, they figure the answer as a team. If they agree, they celebrate their success and move on to the next problem. **Showdown is recommended for practice in logic problems, not for getting started.**

Solo

Students work alone to sequence the cards according to the clues.

Team-Directed Logic Leader

Each team gets their own set of problems and object cards. Rather than the teacher reading the clues, the Logic Leader reads the clues to teammates. Each team leads themselves through the problems at their own pace and checks their work. They switch logic leaders for each new problem.

Team-Pair-Solo

Students work together as a team to solve logic problems until they are certain everyone in the team understands how to solve the problems. Students then break into pairs and solve similar problems using RallyCoach. Then finally, students work alone (Solo) to solve new problems.

Barnyard

Problem 1
1. The rooster is on an end.
2. The cow is not in the middle.
3. The pig is next to the cow.
4. The horse is on the left of the rooster.

Problem 2
1. The horse is not next to the cow.
2. The pig is not next to the rooster.
3. The pig is second.
4. The cow is between the pig and the rooster.

Problem 3
1. The rooster is not last.
2. Two animals are between the cow and rooster.
3. The pig is not next to the rooster.

Problem 4
1. The pig is beside the cow.
2. The cow is beside the horse.
3. The horse is beside the rooster.
4. The rooster is on the far right.

Problem 5
1. The cow is on an end.
2. The horse or pig is on the other end.
3. The rooster is next to the cow.
4. There are only two animals before the pig.

Problem 6
1. The cow is between the rooster and the horse.
2. The pig is on the far right.
3. The pig is not next to the rooster.

Answers
1. Cow, Pig, Horse, Rooster
2. Horse, Pig, Cow, Rooster
3. Rooster, Horse, Pig, Cow
4. Pig, Cow, Horse, Rooster
5. Cow, Rooster, Pig, Horse
6. Rooster, Cow, Horse, Pig

Logic Line-Ups
Kagan Publishing • 1 (800) 933-2667 • www.KaganOnline.com

Cow

Logic Line-Ups
Kagan Publishing • 1 (800) 933-2667 • www.KaganOnline.com

Rooster

Bugs

Problem 1

1. The fly is not in the middle.
2. The bee is not third.
3. The spider is as far away from the fly as possible.
4. The grasshopper is second to last.
5. The spider is to the right of the grasshopper.

Problem 2

1. The spider is not first nor last.
2. The fly is first or last.
3. No bugs are after the grasshopper.
4. The spider is between the fly and bee.

Problem 3

1. The bee is to the right of the fly.
2. Either the fly or grasshopper is last.
3. Either the bee or fly is first.

Problem 4

1. Three bugs are before the grasshopper.
2. No bugs are before the spider.
3. The fly is between the spider and the bee.

Answers

1. Fly, Bee, Grasshopper, Spider
2. Fly, Spider, Bee, Grasshopper
3. Fly, Bee, Spider, Grasshopper
4. Spider, Fly, Bee, Grasshopper
5. Grasshopper, Spider, Fly, Bee
6. Bee, Fly, Spider, Grasshopper

Problem 5

1. The bug that stings is on an end.
2. The bug that spins a web is in the middle.
3. The hopping bug is left of the bug with eight legs.
4. The fly is on the left side of the bee.

Problem 6

1. The bee and the fly are next to each other.
2. The spider and the grasshopper are next to each other.
3. The grasshopper is not next to the bee or fly.
4. The spider is not next to the bee.
5. The grasshopper is not first.

Logic Line-Ups
Kagan Publishing • 1 (800) 933-2667 • www.KaganOnline.com

Bee

Grasshopper

Spider

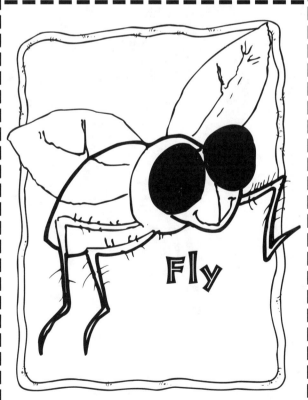

Fly

Bugs

Bee

Logic Line-Ups
Kagan Publishing • 1 (800) 933-2667 • www.KaganOnline.com

Grasshopper

Spider

Logic Line-Ups
Kagan Publishing • 1 (800) 933-2667 • www.KaganOnline.com

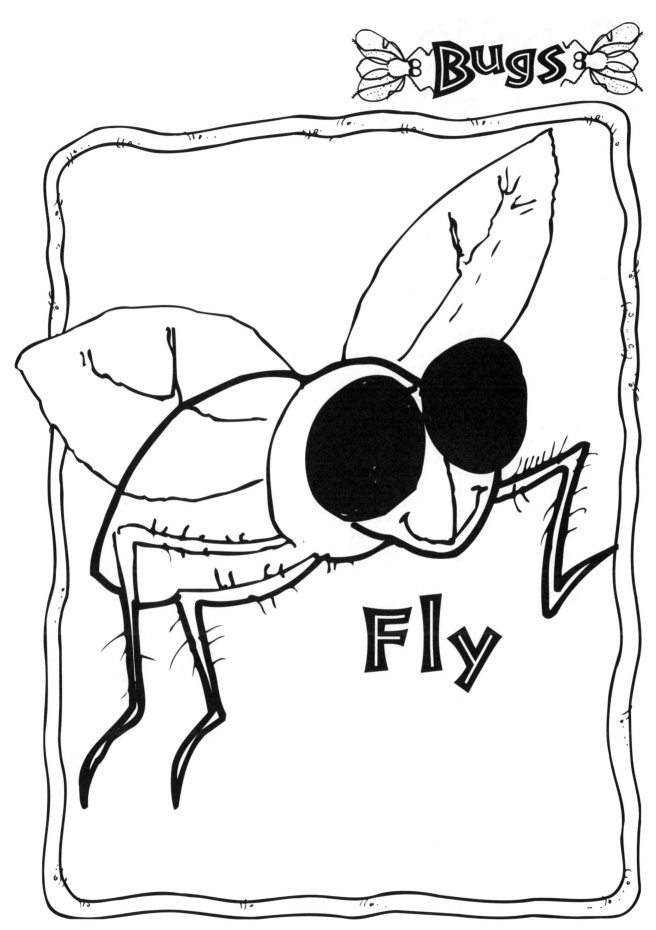

Fly

DINOSAURS

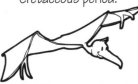

PROBLEM 1
1. The T-Rex is left of the Pterodactyl.
2. The Triceratops is not before the T-Rex.
3. T-Rex and the Brontosaurus are on an end.
4. The Pterodactyl is before the Triceratops.

PROBLEM 2
1. The winged reptile is on an end.
2. The horned dinosaur is on the other end.
3. The heaviest dinosaur is third.
4. The fiercest dinosaur is on the right of the flying reptile.

PROBLEM 3
1. The Brontosaurus is not beside the Pterodactyl.
2. The T-Rex is either first or last.
3. There are two dinosaurs between the T-Rex and the Pterodactyl.
4. The Triceratops is on the left of the Pterodactyl.

PROBLEM 4
1. There are at least two dinosaurs before the T-Rex.
2. The Brontosaurus is not in the middle.
3. The Triceratops is beside the Brontosaurus.
4. The T-Rex is before the Pterodactyl.

PROBLEM 5
1. The Triceratops is not first or third.
2. The Brontosaurus is not third or fourth.
3. The Pterodactyl has three dinosaurs after it.
4. The T-Rex is first or third.

PROBLEM 6
1. The Pterodactyl and the T-Rex are in the middle.
2. The Triceratops is not first and is beside the Pterodactyl.

DINOSAURS

TYRANNOSAURUS REX

TRICERATOPS

PTERODACTYL

BRONTOSAURUS

TYRANNOSAURUS REX

TRICERATOPS

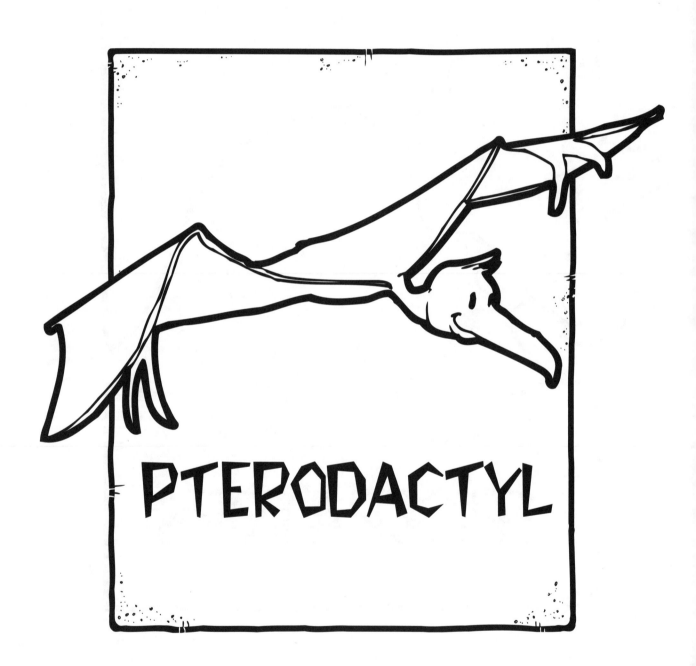

PTERODACTYL

Logic Line-Ups
Kagan Publishing • 1 (800) 933-2667 • www.KaganOnline.com

DINOSAURS

BRONTOSAURUS

Fantasy

Problem 1
1. The dragon is on the opposite side as the unicorn.
2. The magician is the only one next to the unicorn.
3. The princess is on the left of the magician.
4. The dragon is not last.

Problem 2
1. The unicorn is on an end.
2. There is no one to the left of the princess.
3. The magician is next to the princess.

Problem 3
1. The princess is after the unicorn.
2. The dragon is between the magician and unicorn.
3. The unicorn is not on an end.

Problem 4
1. The magician is not third or fourth.
2. The dragon is not first or second.
3. Only one other is next to the unicorn and princess.
4. Either the magician or the dragon is to the right of the unicorn.

Problem 5
1. The king's daughter is between two animals.
2. The horned horse is not on an end.
3. The fire breather is on the opposite end as Merlin, but not first.

Problem 6
1. The unicorn and princess are on the same side.
2. The magician has two others before him.
3. The magician and unicorn are not next to each other.

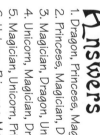

Answers
1. Dragon, Princess, Magician, Unicorn
2. Princess, Magician, Dragon, Unicorn
3. Magician, Dragon, Unicorn, Princess
4. Unicorn, Magician, Dragon, Princess
5. Magician, Unicorn, Princess, Dragon
6. Unicorn, Princess, Magician, Dragon

Logic Line-Ups
Kagan Publishing • 1 (800) 933-2667 • www.KaganOnline.com

Princess

Magician

Dragon

Unicorn

Fantasy

Princess

28

Magician

Fantasy Dragon

Logic Line-Ups
Kagan Publishing • 1 (800) 933-2667 • www.KaganOnline.com

Unicorn

Holidays

■ Problem 1

1. The holidays are in calendar order.

■ Problem 2

1. Easter and Halloween are in the first half.
2. Thanksgiving or Easter is fourth.
3. Independence Day is next to Halloween.

_____

■ Problem 3

1. Two holidays are between Halloween and Thanksgiving.
2. Easter is right after Halloween.

■ Problem 4

1. Easter is either first or second.
2. Halloween is beside Easter.
3. Halloween is not second.
4. Thanksgiving is before Independence Day.

_____

■ Problem 5

1. Independence Day and Halloween have a holiday on both sides.
2. There is only one holiday after Halloween, and it's not Thanksgiving.

■ Problem 6

1. Thanksgiving is not on an end.
2. Easter is right before Halloween.
3. Either Independence Day or Halloween is first.

_____

Answers

1. Easter, Independence Day, Halloween, Thanksgiving
2. Easter, Halloween, Independence Day, Thanksgiving
3. Halloween, Easter, Independence Day, Thanksgiving
4. Thanksgiving, Easter, Halloween, Independence Day
5. Thanksgiving, Independence Day, Halloween, Easter
6. Independence Day, Thanksgiving, Easter, Halloween

Logic Line-Ups
Kagan Publishing • 1 (800) 933-2667 • www.KaganOnline.com

Easter

Logic Line-Ups
Kagan Publishing • 1 (800) 933-2667 • www.KaganOnline.com

Independence Day

Thanksgiving

Logic Line-Ups
Kagan Publishing • 1 (800) 933-2667 • www.KaganOnline.com

Halloween

nutrition

Problem 2
1. Neither the cheese nor bread are next to the ham.
2. The apple is not next to the cheese.
3. The cheese is not second, third, nor fourth.

Problem 1
1. The fruit is before the meat.
2. The grain is right after the dairy.
3. The fruit and grain are on opposite ends.

Problem 3
1. The apple is in the first half.
2. The ham is not in the second half.
3. The cheese is next to the apple.

Problem 4
1. The ham is between the apple and bread.
2. The apple is not on an end.
3. Bread is not first.

Problem 5
1. The bread and apple are in the first half.
2. The ham and bread are not next to each other.
3. The bread and cheese are not next to each other.
4. The apple and ham are not next to each other.

Problem 6
1. Joe ate a ham and cheese sandwich before the apple.
2. He nibbled on ham before he ate the sandwich.
3. Joe had a bite of cheese, then took his first bite of the sandwich.

Answers
1. Apple, Ham, Cheese, Bread
2. Cheese, Bread, Apple, Ham
3. Ham, Apple, Cheese, Bread
4. Cheese, Apple, Ham, Bread
5. Bread, Apple, Cheese, Ham
6. Ham, Cheese, Bread, Apple

Logic Line-Ups
Kagan Publishing • 1 (800) 933-2667 • www.KaganOnline.com

nutrition

Apple

Bread

Cheese

Ham

Apple

Bread

Cheese

Ham

Occupations

Problem 1

1. The farmer is not in the middle.
2. The mechanic is first.
3. The fire fighter is to the right of the mechanic.

Problem 2

1. The nurse is on an end.
2. The farmer is to the left of the mechanic.
3. The mechanic is on the far right.

Problem 3

1. The fire fighter is not next to the mechanic.
2. The nurse is to the left of the fire fighter.
3. The farmer is to the left of the mechanic.
4. The mechanic is second.

Problem 4

1. The nurse is next to the farmer.
2. The farmer is on an end.
3. The fire fighter is on the other end.
4. The mechanic is to the right of the fire fighter.

Problem 5

1. The mechanic is not last or in the middle.
2. The nurse not in the middle.
3. The farmer is after the fire fighter.

Problem 6

1. The mechanic is not first or last.
2. The nurse is first or last.
3. The fire fighter is on the left side of the nurse.

Answers

1. Mechanic, Fire Fighter, Nurse, Farmer
2. Nurse, Fire Fighter, Farmer, Mechanic
3. Farmer, Mechanic, Nurse, Fire Fighter
4. Fire Fighter, Mechanic, Nurse, Farmer
5. Mechanic, Fire Fighter, Farmer, Nurse
6. Farmer, Mechanic, Fire Fighter, Nurse

Logic Line-Ups
Kagan Publishing • 1 (800) 933-2667 • www.KaganOnline.com

Mechanic

Fire Fighter

Nurse

Farmer

Mechanic

Logic Line-Ups
Kagan Publishing • 1 (800) 933-2667 • www.KaganOnline.com

Fire Fighter

Nurse

Logic Line-Ups
Kagan Publishing • 1 (800) 933-2667 • www.KaganOnline.com

Farmer

 # uter Space

Aliens, a space rover, an astronaut and a planet are lost in space. Can you help the astronomer figure out where they are?

 # Problem 1

1. The aliens and the astronaut are right next to each other.
2. The planet is after the space rover.
3. The space rover is right after the astronaut.

 # Problem 2

1. The space rover is not on an end.
2. The aliens are as far from the planet as possible.
3. Either the aliens or space rover are last.
4. The astronaut is closest to the planet.

 # Problem 3

1. Neither the aliens nor the planet are on an end.
2. The space rover is not last.
3. The space rover is not beside the planet.

 # Problem 4

1. The living beings are on the ends.
2. The astronaut is closer to the space rover than the aliens.
3. Mercury is after the vehicle.

 # Problem 5

1. The aliens are next to the planet, but not first.
2. The aliens are next to the astronaut, but not last.
3. The aliens are not in third.
4. Both the astronaut and the space rover are on the right of the alien.

 # Problem 6

1. No one is between the space rover and astronaut.
2. No one is between the planet and space rover.
3. No one is between the aliens and planet.
4. The aliens are not last.

 ## Answers

1. Aliens, Astronaut, Space Rover, Planet
2. Planet, Astronaut, Space Rover, Aliens
3. Space Rover, Aliens, Planet, Astronaut
4. Astronaut, Space Rover, Planet, Aliens
5. Planet, Aliens, Astronaut, Space Rover
6. Aliens, Planet, Space Rover, Astronaut

Logic Line-Ups
Kagan Publishing • 1 (800) 933-2667 • www.KaganOnline.com

Planet

Astronaut

Space Rover

Aliens

Planet

Logic Line-Ups
Kagan Publishing • 1 (800) 933-2667 • www.KaganOnline.com

Astronaut

Space Rover

Aliens

Problem 1

1. The cat and the bird are not next to each other.
2. The rabbit is not first or in the middle.
3. Neither the bird nor dog are next to the rabbit.

Problem 2

1. Only the bird is next to the cat.
2. The rabbit is as far from the cat as possible.
3. The dog is second.

Problem 3

1. There are two animals between the cat and bird.
2. Either the cat or rabbit is first.
3. The dog is between the rabbit and bird.

Problem 4

1. The barking animal is second or fourth.
2. The feline is not first or third.
3. The bunny is right next to the doggy.
4. The flying pet is only next to the cat.

Problem 5

1. The cat is not in the middle.
2. The rabbit is in the first half.
3. The bird and cat are in the second half.
4. The dog is farther from the cat than the rabbit is.

Problem 6

1. The bird and cat are not next to each other.
2. The dog and rabbit are not next to each other.
3. The dog is second.
4. The bird and rabbit are next to each other.

answers

1. Bird, Dog, Cat, Rabbit
2. Rabbit, Dog, Bird, Cat
3. Cat, Rabbit, Dog, Bird
4. Bird, Cat, Rabbit, Dog
5. Dog, Rabbit, Bird, Cat
6. Cat, Dog, Bird, Rabbit

Cat

Dog

Bird

Rabbit

Bird

Rabbit

Seasons

Problem 1

The seasons are in chronological order beginning with winter.

Problem 2

1. Winter and Fall are not in the second half.
2. Summer is before Spring.
3. Either Spring or Fall is first.

Problem 3

1. December is after July.
2. October is before January.
3. April is after February.
4. Either August or March is first.

Problem 4

1. Summer is after Fall.
2. Winter is after Spring.
3. Summer is either first or second.

Problem 5

1. There is one season between Spring and Summer.
2. There is one season between Fall and Winter.
3. There are two seasons between Spring and Winter.
4. Fall is beside Spring.
5. There are no seasons after Winter.

Problem 6

1. Fall is next to Spring.
2. Summer is next to Winter.
3. Spring is next to Summer.
4. Fall is not first.

answers

1. Winter, Spring, Summer, Fall
2. Fall, Winter, Summer, Spring
3. Summer, Fall, Winter, Spring
4. Fall, Summer, Spring, Winter
5. Spring, Fall, Summer, Winter
6. Winter, Summer, Spring, Fall

Logic Line-Ups
Kagan Publishing • 1 (800) 933-2667 • www.KaganOnline.com

Winter

Spring

Summer

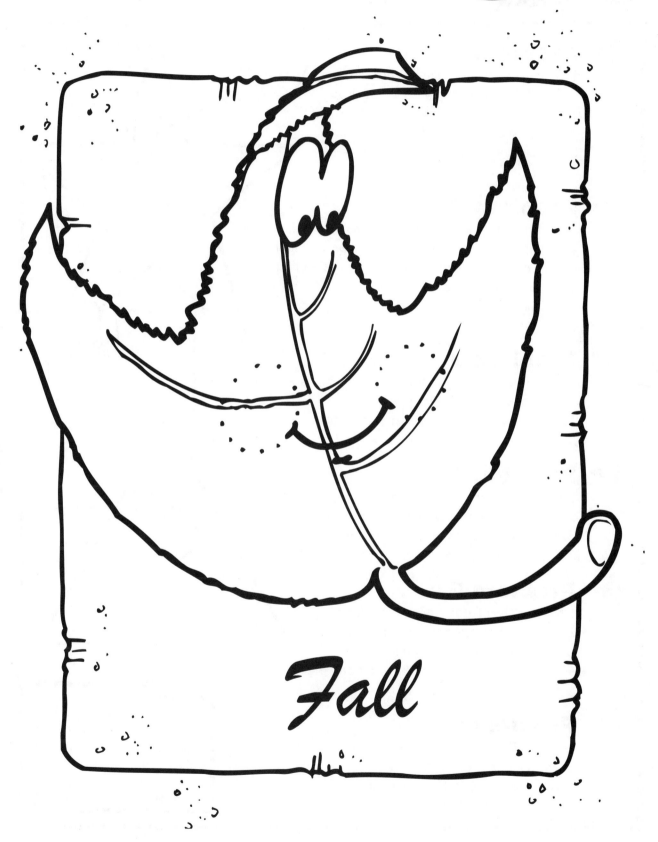

Fall

SHAPES

▶ ## Problem 1
1. The shape with no points is not last.
2. The shape with five points is not first.
3. The shape with three points is on an end.
4. The star is not second or last.
5. The circular shape is not in the middle.

▶ ## Problem 2
1. The shape with three sides is in the first half.
2. The shape with four sides is in the second half.
3. Only one shape is between the triangle and square.
4. The star is not second or third.
5. Neither the circle nor star is first.

▶ ## Problem 3
1. The two shapes with three sides or fewer are in the middle.
2. The shape with the most points is not last.
3. The round shape is not next to the star.

▶ ## Problem 4
1. The triangle and star are before the circle.
2. The triangle and star are after the square.
3. The triangle is between the circle and star.

▶ ## Problem 5
1. Neither the star nor square are first.
2. Neither the circle nor star are last.
3. Either the star or square is last.
4. The triangle is between the circle and star.

▶ ## Problem 6
1. The circle is next to the square.
2. The star is next to the circle.
3. The triangle is next to the star.
4. The star is not third.

ANSWERS
1. Circle, Square, Star, Triangle
2. Triangle, Circle, Square, Star
3. Star, Triangle, Circle, Square
4. Square, Star, Triangle, Circle
5. Circle, Triangle, Star, Square
6. Triangle, Star, Circle, Square

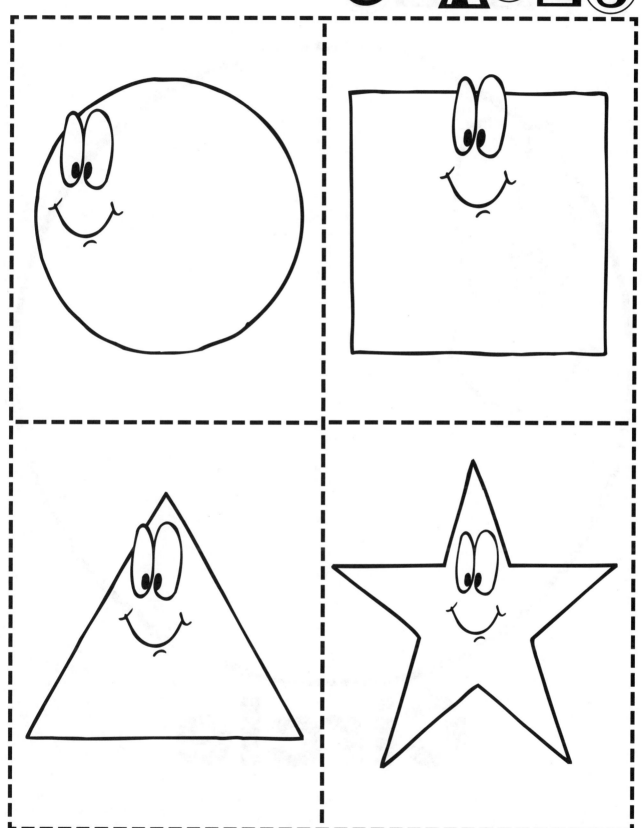

SHAPES

Circle

Logic Line-Ups
Kagan Publishing • 1 (800) 933-2667 • www.KaganOnline.com

Square

SHAPES

Triangle

Logic Line-Ups
Kagan Publishing • 1 (800) 933-2667 • www.KaganOnline.com

Star

Under the Sea

Problem 1

1. The human is not last.
2. The shark is second or third.
3. The fish is one before the end.

Problem 2

1. The shark is not first.
2. Neither the diver nor the fish are on an end.
3. The fish is not between the diver and the shark.

Problem 3

1. The one with tentacles is not on an end.
2. The one with two legs is right after the octopus.
3. The diver is not fourth.
4. The one with a rigid triangular dorsal fin is not first.

Problem 4

1. Only the shark is next to the one wearing a suit.
2. Only the one that releases an ink cloud for safety is next to the fish.
3. The diver is not after the shark.

Problem 5

1. Two are between the fish and shark.
2. The one with suckers is not second.
3. The fish and octopus are not next to each other.

Problem 6

1. The one without a backbone is not last.
2. The octopus is not second.
3. The fish and octopus are not next to each other.
4. The diver is not second.
5. The fish is right before the diver.

Answers

1. Diver, Shark, Fish, Octopus
2. Octopus, Fish, Diver, Shark
3. Fish, Octopus, Diver, Shark
4. Diver, Shark, Octopus, Fish
5. Fish, Diver, Octopus, Shark
6. Octopus, Shark, Fish, Diver

Under the Sea

diver

fish

octopus

shark

diver

Logic Line-Ups
Kagan Publishing • 1 (800) 933-2667 • www.KaganOnline.com

fish

octopus

shark

How To Make Your Own Problems

1 Write down the answer first.

2 Write a clue and draw out the possibilities. Use the spatial vocabulary (next page) to write your clues.

3 Continue writing clues and drawing out the possibilities until only the correct answer is possible.

4 Check your clues by solving the problem.

Example

Write the answer first   →   H   A   C   B
Ham, Apple, Cheese, Bread.
‾‾‾‾‾ ‾‾‾‾‾ ‾‾‾‾‾ ‾‾‾‾‾

1. The apple is in the first half.   A   A
The apple is either first or second.

2. The ham is not in the second half.   AH   AH
Either the apple or ham is first or second.

3. The cheese is next to the apple.
The apple must be second, because if it was first,
it would only be next to the ham. The cheese must
be third since it can't be on the other side of the
apple. That's where the ham is. Therefore, the
bread must be last.

Logic Line-Ups
Kagan Publishing • 1 (800) 933-2667 • www.KaganOnline.com

Some Spatial Vocabulary

Here are some different ways to describe the location of items. You or your students may use this spatial vocabulary to come up with new problems. Can you think of other ways to describe the locations?

On One End
only one next to
not in the middle
on an end
not second or third
as far away as possible

First
first
not last or in the middle
far left

Last
last or fourth
is not first or in the middle
far right

In the Middle
second or third
not first or last
not first or fourth
not on an end

More Vocabulary
neither
either
first half
second half
to the right of
to the left of
not next to
next to
before
not before
after
not after
beside
not beside
not between
between
two _____ are between
two _____ are before
one _____ is before
one _____ is after

The 24 Ways To Sequence Four Items

If you make your own problems or have students make their own, it may be helpful to know that there are 24 possible ways to sequence four items. If you're not careful, there may be more correct answers than you think! (Or maybe you want more than one correct answer.)

Statistically speaking, the way to calculate the possible sequences for four items is as follows: 1 x 2 x 3 x 4 = 24. For five: 1 x 2 x 3 x 4 x 5 = 120! Let your students calculate the possibilities for 2, 3, 4, 5, and more...

Below is an illustration of all 24 possible sequences for the numbers 1, 2, 3, 4.

One First	Two First	Three First	Four First
1234	2134	3124	4123
1243	2143	3142	4132
1324	2314	3214	4213
1342	2341	3241	4231
1423	2413	3412	4321
1432	2431	3421	4312

Logic Line-Ups
Kagan Publishing • 1 (800) 933-2667 • www.KaganOnline.com

Send A Problem

Have students work in teams to come up with their own problems. Teams send their problems to another team to solve using Logic Line-Ups.

More Sequencing Ideas

In addition to having students line up to solve the problems, students can line up based on other characteristics relating to their cards, such as:

- Height
- Weight
- Width
- Alphabetical order
- Number of letters in name
- Distance (planets from sun, states)
- Value (coins, objects)
- Speed (transportation, ocean life, pets)
- Noise
- Intelligence (pets)
- Temperature (seasons)
- Number of Faces (shapes)
- Number of legs, wings (bugs)
- Amount of fat, calories, carbos (nutrition)

Students can also arrange themselves based on subjective characteristics such as:

- Importance
- Preference
- Difficulty (occupations)
- Danger (occupations, ocean life)

Can you think of more ways to have students sequence themselves?

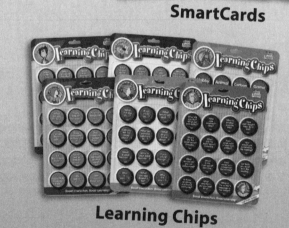